Circle the letter Aa in the words above.

Find and color the pictures that begin with the Aa sound.

Balloons for Baby Bear

Circle the letter Bb in the words above.

Color the balloon if the picture begins with the Bb sound.

Name the pictures in each row. Circle the ones that begin with the Bb sound.

b

b

Trace each word. Say the word.

Draw the path to the big blue ox.

A cup for Carl Camel

Circle the letter Cc in the words above.

Say the name of each picture. Circle the ones that begin with the Cc sound.

Write c to make a word that rhymes with the one on the left. Say the word.

rake

boat

___oat

bat

___at

horn

___orn

Circle the letter Dd in the words above.

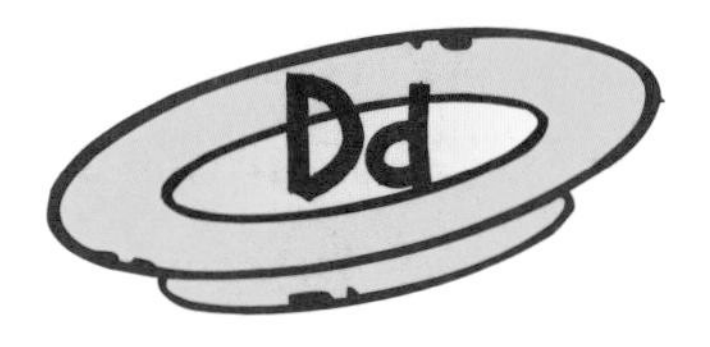

Help the dog find the doghouse. Color the circle if the picture begins with the Dd sound.

Say the name of each picture.
Draw lines from the dragon to the ones that begin with the Dd sound.

Trace each word. Say the word.

Draw the path to the diamonds.

Circle the letter Ee in the words above.

Say the name of each picture. Color the square if the picture begins with the EE sound.

Frank's funny faucet

Circle the letter Ff in the words above.

Say the name of each picture. Color the space if the picture begins with the Ff sound.

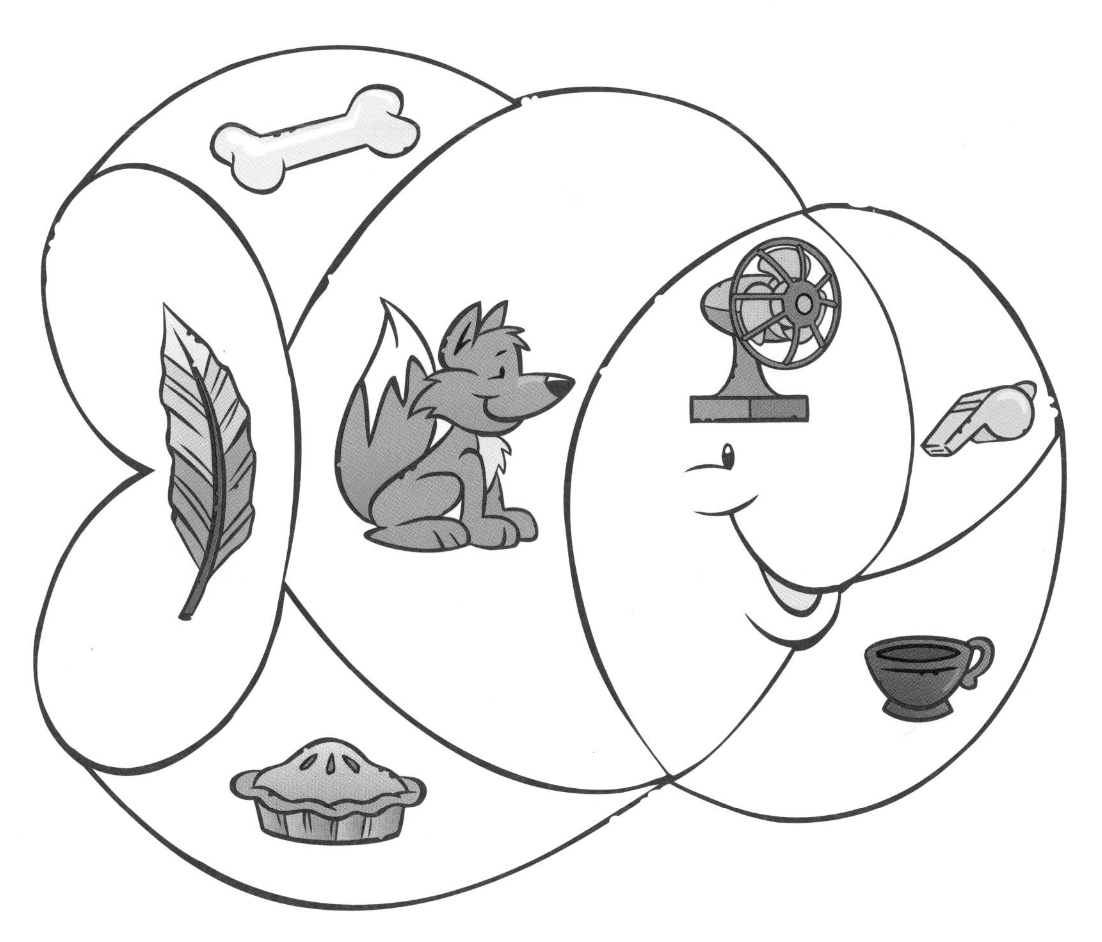

Write f to finish each word.
Say the word.

Find and color the pictures of the words you just wrote.

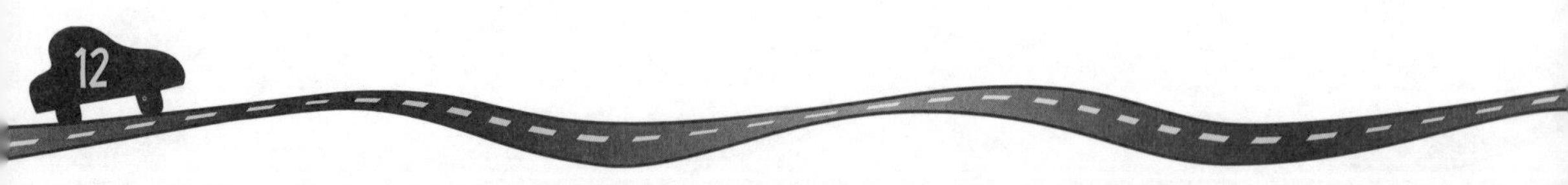

Find What Starts with Ff

Circle the word for the picture. Color the ones that begin with the Ff sound.

five

live

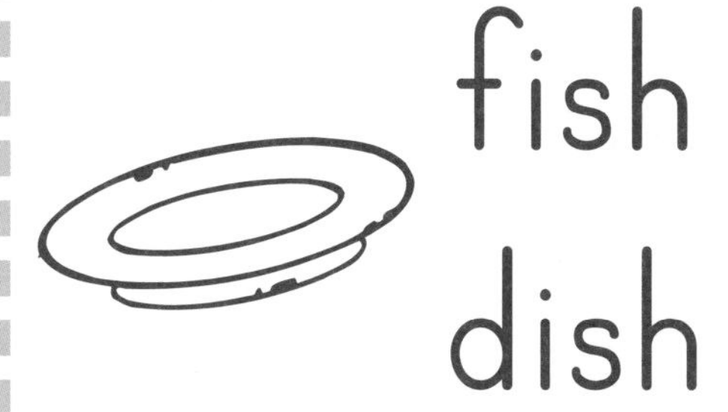

fish

dish

box

fox

race

face

man

fan

fire

tire

Goose and the garden gate

Circle the letter Gg in the words above.

Say the name of each picture.
Draw lines to the letter it begins with.

Say the name of each picture.
Draw lines from the ghost to the ones that begin with the Gg sound.

Look at each picture. Trace the word to finish each rhyme.

a 

in a coat

a loose goose

Circle the letter Hh in the words above.

Say the name of each picture. Draw lines from Hh to the ones that begin with the Hh sound.

Name the pictures in each row. Circle the ones that begin with the Hh sound.

h

h

Trace each word. Say the word.

horse

hen

harp

hat

Circle the letter Ii in the words above.

Say the name of each picture. Color the space if the picture begins with the Ii sound.

Circle the letter Jj in the words above.

Say the name of each picture. Color the ones that begin with the Jj sound.

Say the name of each picture. Circle the ones that begin with the Jj sound.

Write j to make a word that rhymes with the one on the left.

net

___et

ham

___am

Draw faces on the pumpkins to make jack-o-lanterns.

Trace each word. Say the word.

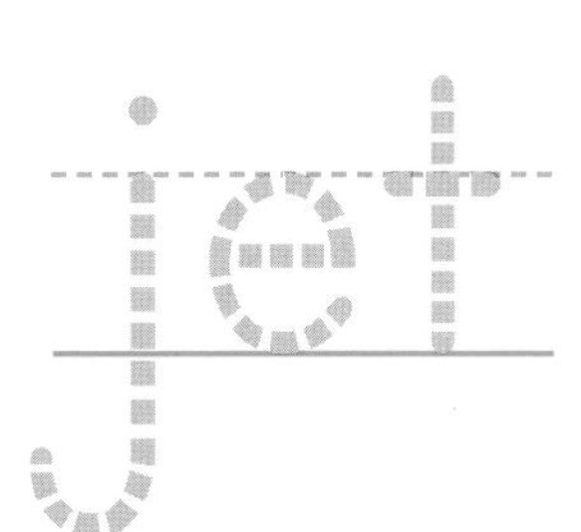

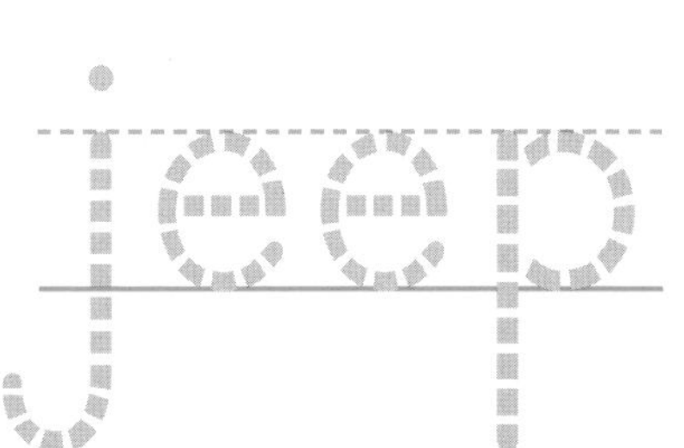

Circle the letter Kk in the words above.

Say the name of each picture. Color the ones that begin with the Kk sound.

Write k to finish each word.
Say the word.

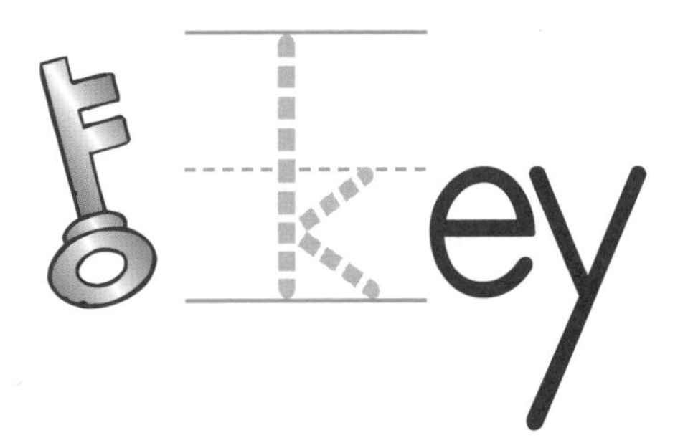

ing

Find and color the pictures of
the words you just wrote.

K is the Key

Say the name of each picture.
Draw lines from the key to the ones that begin with the Kk sound.

Trace each word. Say the word.

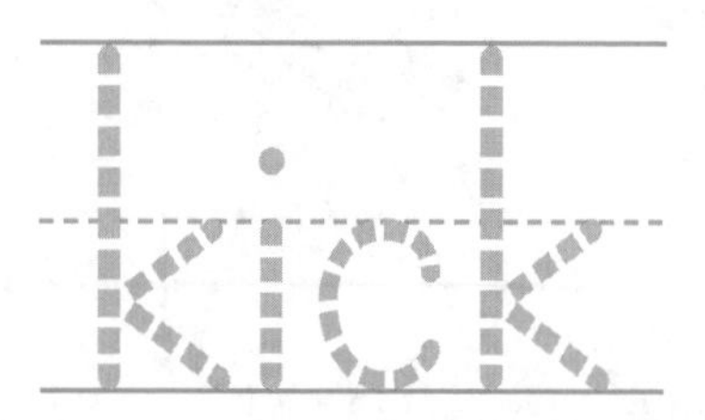

Circle the letter Ll in the words above.

Find and color the pictures that begin with the Ll sound.

Write l to finish each word. Say the word. Find and color the pictures of the words you just wrote.

l og

_ eaf

_ ock

_ amb

_ adder

Draw the path from the lamb to its mother.

Circle the letter Mm in the words above.

Color the pictures that begin with the Mm sound to make the path to the cheese.

Write m to finish each word.
Say the word.

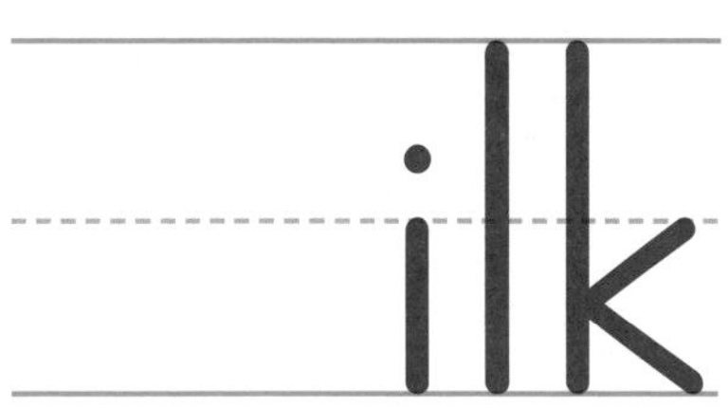

ice

Write m next to the picture that begins with the Mm sound.

Find and color the pictures that begin with the Mm sound.

A needle for Nurse Nancy

Circle the letter Nn in the words above.

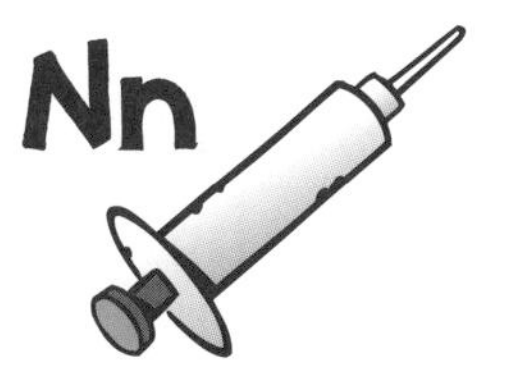

Say the name of each picture. Draw lines from Nn to the ones that begin with the Nn sound.

Find and color the pictures that begin with the Nn sound.

Trace each word. Say the word.

Find and color 3 nests.
Color the rest of the picture.

Circle the letter Oo in the words above.

Say the name of each picture. Circle the letter it begins with.

A puppet for Patty Pig

Circle the letter Pp in the words above.

Say the name of each picture. Draw lines from Pp to the ones that begin with the Pp sound.

Write p to finish each word.
Say the word. Find and color
the pictures of the words
you just wrote.

Find and color the pictures that begin with the Pp sound.

Circle the letter Qq in the words above.

Connect the dots from A to Q. Use the code to color the pictures on the quilt.

Things that begin with A a

Things that begin with Hh

Things that begin with Qq

Say the name of each picture. Draw lines from the ? to the ones that begin with the Qq sound.

Trace each word. Say the word.

Draw the path from the queen to the quilt.

Circle the letter Rr in the words above.

Use the code to color Rick Robot. Find and color the pictures in Rick's rocket that begin with the Rr sound.

R = 

r = 

Say the name of each picture. Color the ones that begin with the Rr sound.

Write r next to each picture that begins with the Rr sound.

Find and color the pictures that begin with the Rr sound.

Seal plays in the sun

Circle the letter Ss in the words above.

Say the name of each picture. Circle the ones that begin with the Ss sound.

Write s to finish each word.
Say the word.

s aw

___ un

___ ock

___ ix

Write s next to the picture that begins with the Ss sound.

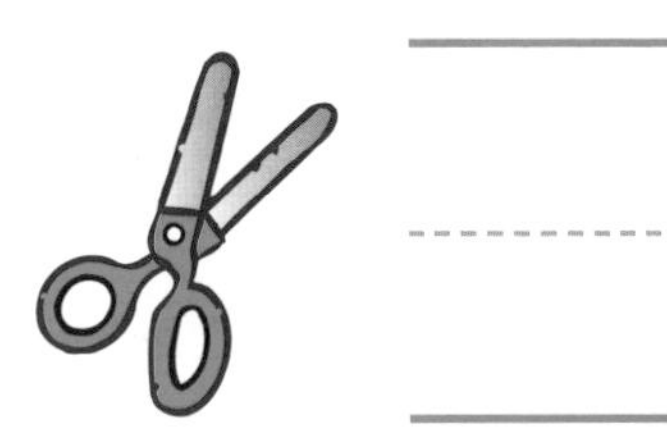

Find and color 3 [snake]s.
Color the rest of the picture.

Turtle is on the telephone

Circle the letter Tt in the words above.

Say the name of each picture. Color the ones that begin with the Tt sound.

Name the pictures in each row. Circle the ones that begin with the Tt sound.

Trace each word. Say the word.

Find and color the pictures that begin with the Tt sound.

An umbrella for Umpire

Circle the letter Uu in the words above.

Use the code to color the picture.

R = S = T = U =

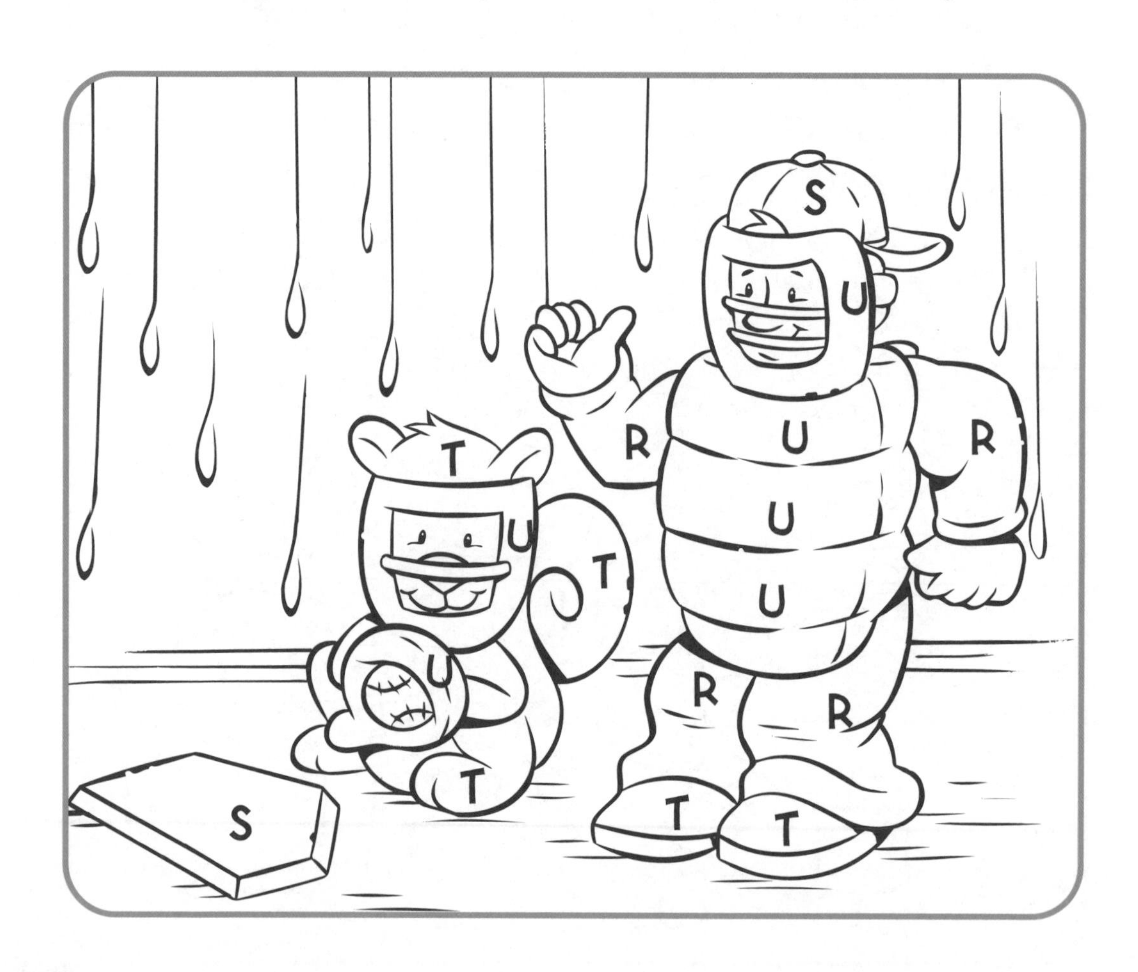

Circle the letter Vv in the words above.

Say the name of each picture. Color the ones that begin with the Vv sound.

Name the pictures in each row. Circle the ones that begin with the Vv sound.

Trace each word. Say the word.

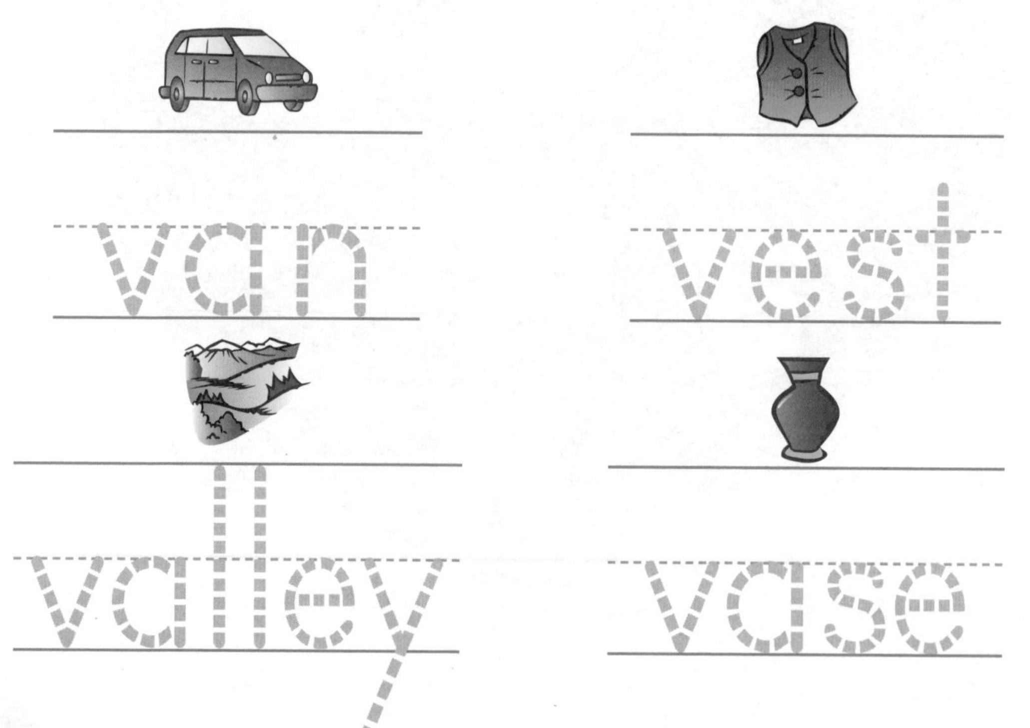

Connect the dots from A to V.
Color the picture.

Witch watches the web

Circle the letter Ww in the words above.

Say the name of each picture.
Draw lines from the web to the ones that begin with the Ww sound.

Name the pictures in each row. Circle the ones that begin with the Ww sound.

W

w

Look at each picture. Trace the word to finish each rhyme.

a pig in a wig

a dragon in a

Extra X-rays of Max

Circle the letter Xx in the words above.

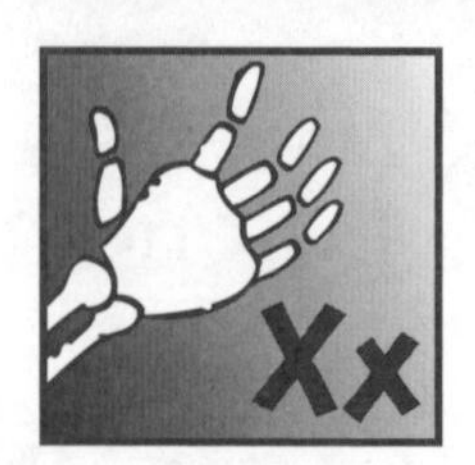

Draw lines to connect each body part with its X-ray.

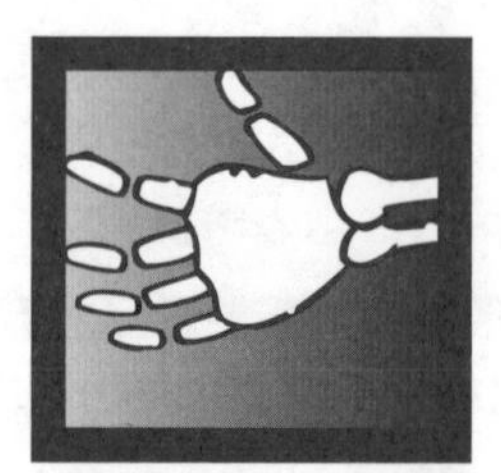

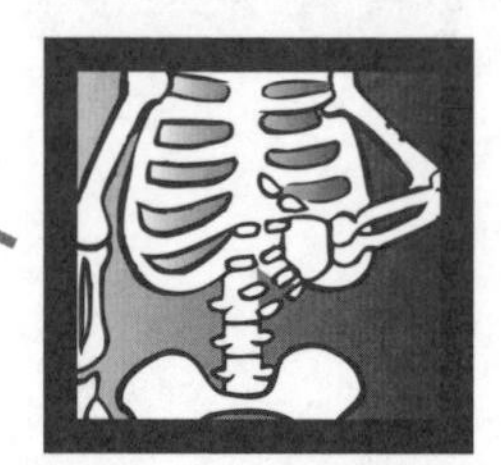

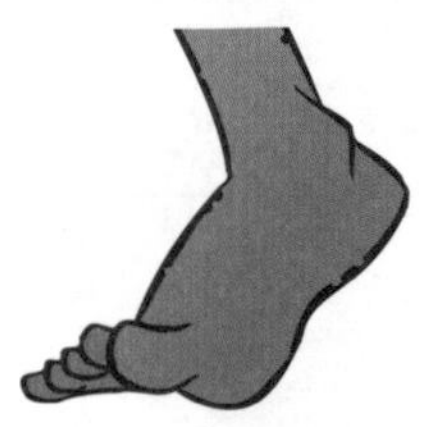

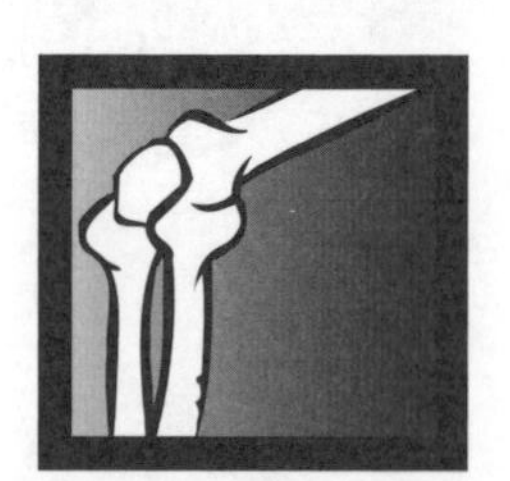

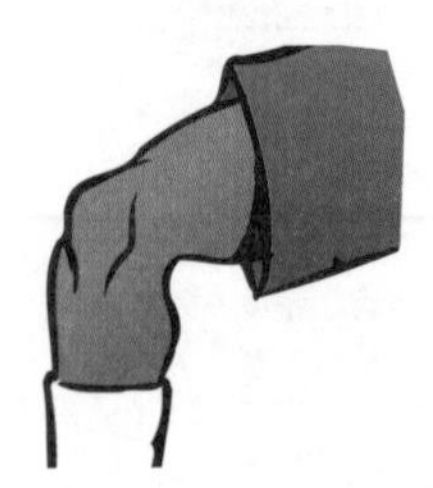

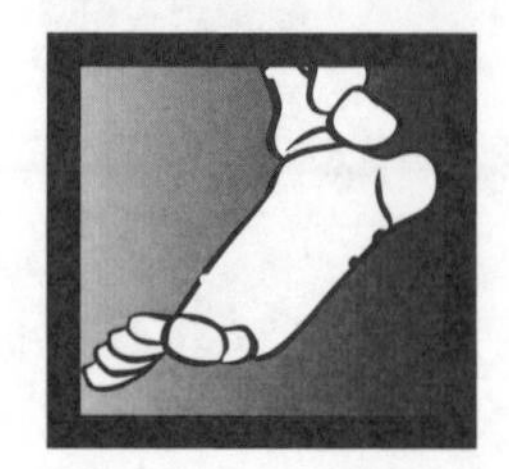

Yaks in Lynn's yard

Circle the letter Yy in the words above.

Say the name of each picture. Color the ones that begin with the Yy sound.

Trace each word. Say the word.

Circle the correct answer.

What goes up and down but never gives you a ride?

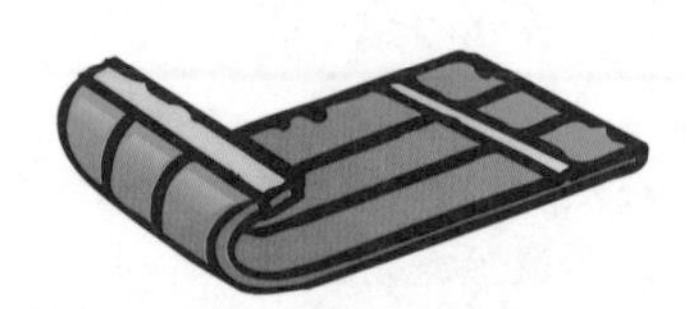

Circle the letter Zz in the words above.

Draw the path from Aa to Zz to help the zebra find the zoo.

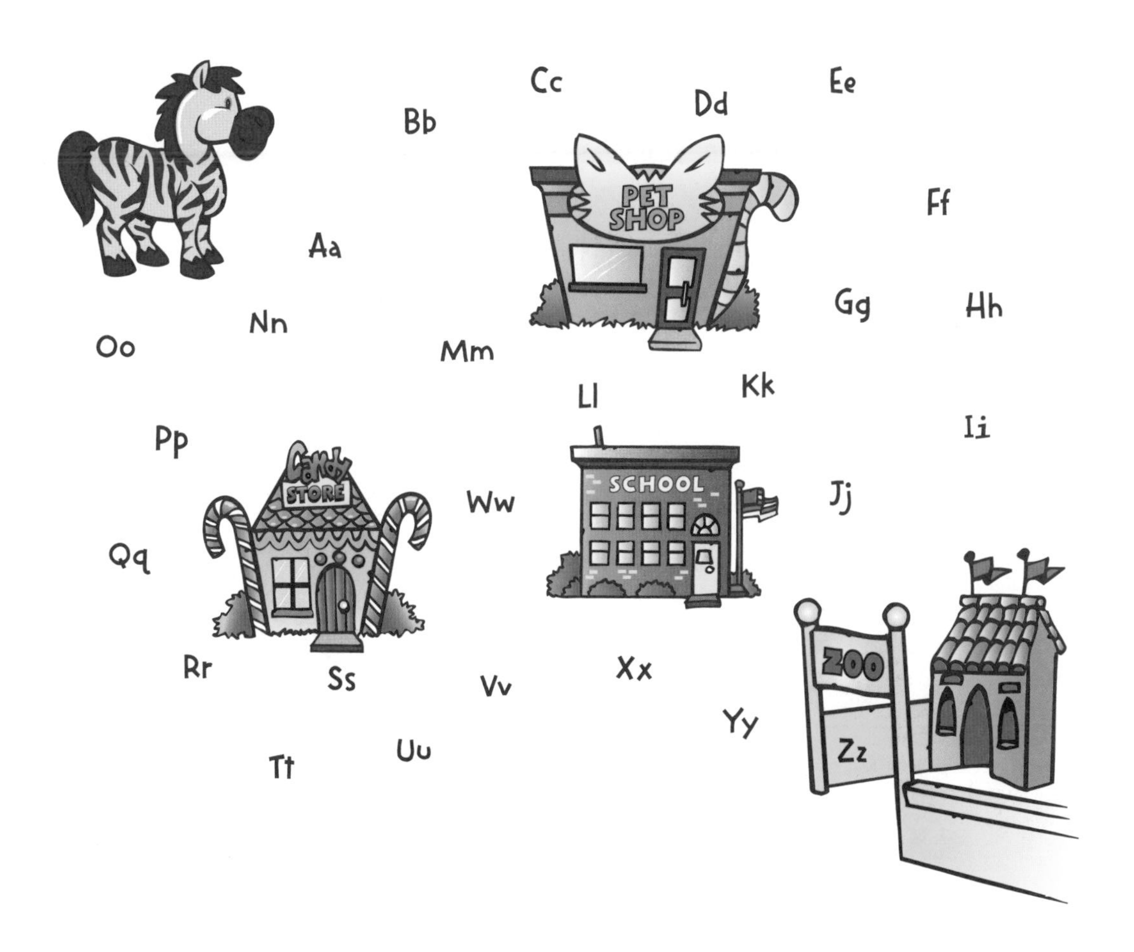

Say the name of each picture. Color the ones that begin with the Zz sound.

Trace each word. Say the word.

Find and color 5 [zebra]s.
Color the rest of the picture.

Say the name of each picture.
Color the picture if its name begins with the letter in the box.

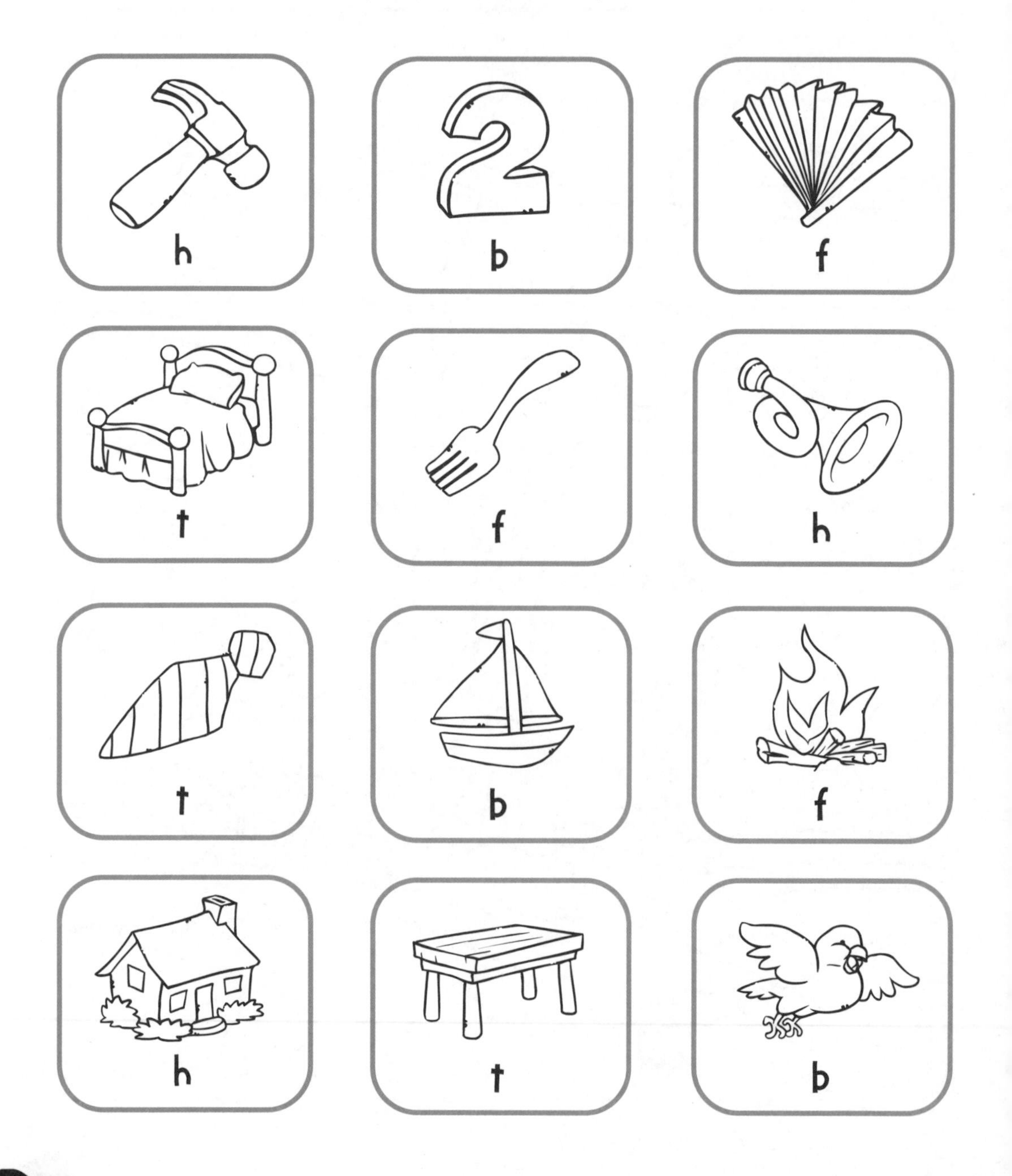

Use the code to color the pictures that begin with the sound of:

c =  m = 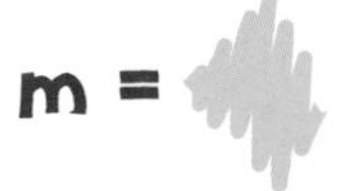 n =  r =

Say the name of each picture. Fill in the circle if its name begins with the letter at the beginning of the row.